Contents

Writing in sentences

You can put words together to make a **sentence**.
A sentence must be complete and make sense.

Matilda made a loaf of bread.

Try it

1 Say and then write a complete **sentence** using these words.

play outside _____

bunch of flowers _____

cats and dogs _____

see stars _____

Charlie _____

2 Write a **sentence** to follow each sentence below. Use the word
'**and**' in your sentences.

Oscar found a silver coin. _____

_____

Daisy the dog ran into the woods. _____

_____

Pedro forgot to turn off the tap. _____

_____

Sentence practice

Write the next <u>two</u> sentences. Use the word '**and**' in one sentence.

Ethan woke up early one morning. _____

_____

Sentence punctuation

All sentences start with a **capital letter**. Most sentences end with a **full stop**. Some sentences end with a **question mark** or an **exclamation mark**.

The little rabbit began to worry. Where could Ben be?

Try it

1. Write in the missing **punctuation marks**.

We went to the zoo Jacob was very excited.

The clown did a clever trick and Abdul laughed at him

Gran came to visit us last Monday Grandpa came too.

Who was knocking at the door Max went to see.

He made a boat out of wood and sailed it on the sea

2. Here is part of a story. The **sentence punctuation** is missing. Write the story using the correct punctuation.

The children went to find Nina they looked in the garden and they looked in the shed they looked everywhere where was Nina

_____

_____

_____

Sentence practice

Write three sentences about your favourite toy.

_____

_____

_____

Joining words: 'and', 'but'

The words 'and' and 'but' are **joining words**. They join together two sentences to make one longer sentence.

She saw the porridge and it smelt delicious.

She tasted the porridge but it was too hot.

Try it

1 Choose the best **joining word**, 'and' or 'but', to complete each sentence.

She opened the door _____ they went inside.

I can swim a width _____ I cannot dive in.

Ali found a wooden chest _____ it was locked.

A car came down the road _____ it stopped outside.

He waited _____ he waited _____ no-one came.

2 Add the **joining word 'but'** and then complete each **sentence**.

The rabbit was only small _____

I like grapes _____

I wanted to go skating _____

Lucy was winning the race _____

A spider has eight legs _____

Sentence practice

Write a sentence about a monster using the word 'but'.

_____

Joining words: 'or'

Remember

The word '**or**' is another **joining word**. You can use 'or' to join two words or to join two sentences to make one longer sentence.

Do you like porridge hot or cold?

We can eat the porridge now or we can go for a walk.

Try it

1 Choose the best **joining word**, '**or**', '**and**' or '**but**', to complete each sentence.

We can stay here _____ we can go to the park.

You must go now _____ the giant will eat you.

I went to buy some jam _____ the shop was shut.

The mouse saw the cat _____ it ran and hid.

Take the cake out of the oven _____ it will burn.

2 Add the **joining word 'or'** and then complete each **sentence**.

We could hide in the shed _____

Apples can be red _____

It might rain _____

We can play inside _____

The box is under the bed _____

Sentence practice

Write a sentence about what you might do after school. Use the word '**or**'.

_____

Verbs: past and present tense 1

Verbs are doing words. Verbs can be in the **past tense** or the **present tense**. The **tense** of the verb shows when it happened.

I open the door.   (present tense – happening now)
I open<u>ed</u> the door.   (past tense – happened in the past)

Try it

1   Underline the **verb** in each of these sentences. Write whether it is in the **past tense** or the **present tense**.

Thunder boomed across the roof tops. _____ tense

Caterpillars turn into butterflies. _____ tense

He followed the trail of stones. _____ tense

The girl jumps into the stream. _____ tense

2   The **verbs** in these sentences are in the **present tense**. Rewrite each sentence in the **past tense**.

I count six trees. _____

He waits for the bus. _____

Ellie scores a goal. _____

Sam crosses the road. _____

We share the sweets. _____

Sentence practice

Write <u>two</u> sentences using the **verb** 'walk'. Write one in the **present tense** and one in the **past tense**.

_____

_____

Verbs: past and present tense 2

Lots of **past tense verbs** end with **–ed** but sometimes the word changes in a different way.

I run down the road.   (present tense)
I ran down the road.   (past tense)

Try it

1 Write the **verb** from each sentence in the **past tense**.

The boy <u>falls</u> off the slide. _____

I <u>have</u> toast for breakfast. _____

I <u>see</u> a snail in the garden. _____

Three fish <u>swim</u> across the lake. _____

The nice lady <u>makes</u> cakes for tea. _____

2 Underline the <u>two</u> **present tense verbs** in each sentence. Then rewrite the sentence in the **past tense**.

I take an apple to school and eat it at lunchtime.

_____

It is hot so Erin wears her shorts.

_____

The wind blows and the rain comes down.

_____

Sentence practice

Write a sentence using the **past tense** of the **verb** 'fly'.

_____

Statements

A **statement** is a sentence that tells you something. Statements often start with who or what the sentence is about, followed by a **verb**.

Pandas eat bamboo.

Try it

1 Put the words and punctuation in order so they make a **statement**.

in live the sea Whales . _____

plate Rory a . broke _____

brown eyes . have I _____

curtains . Kara the opened _____

leaves The had tree . no _____

2 Complete these **statements**.

_____ count in twos and tens.

The cook _____ the eggs in a pan of water.

Zebras _____   _____

_____ the washing on the line.

_____ proud and happy.

Sentence practice

Write a **statement** about what you are wearing.

_____

_____

Questions

A **question** is a sentence that asks something. Questions start with question words or sometimes with **verbs** such as 'Can' and 'Do'. Questions end with a **question mark**.

<u>Where</u> did the cow jump?   <u>Can</u> cows jump?

Try it

1 Add a word to complete each **question**. Then complete the answer.

Question	Statement
_____ is your name?	My name _____
_____ lost a glass slipper?	_____ a glass slipper.
_____ it going to snow?	Yes, _____
_____ you like pizza?	_____ like pizza.
_____ owls fly?	Yes, _____

2 Here is a **statement**. Write some **questions** about it.

Jim went to the shop.

Why _____

When _____

How _____

Did _____

Is _____

Sentence practice

Write a **statement** and a **question** about frogs.

_____

Exclamations

Try it

1 Some of these sentences are **exclamations** and some are **questions**. Write in the missing **punctuation marks**.

How amazing_____

How old are you_____

What a pity_____

What a surprise_____

What will you do now_____

2 Write an **exclamation** to follow each **statement**.

Billy dropped the cake.	What _____
I have won a prize.	How _____
Let me help you with that.	How _____
I have picked some flowers for you.	How _____
All the wolf cubs began to howl.	What _____

Sentence practice

Write a **statement** and an **exclamation** about a game of football.

_____

_____

Commands

Remember

A **command** is a sentence that instructs or tells someone to do something. Commands often start with a **verb**.

Clean the grate.   Make the fire.

Try it

1 Are these sentences **statements** or **commands**? Write 'statement' or 'command'.

Stop doing that.   _____

The car made a terrible noise.   _____

Don't let the dog off its lead.   _____

Rowan plays with the hamster.   _____

Plants need water to grow.   _____

2 Complete these **commands** with a suitable **verb**.

_____ the dice to start the game.

_____ the hammer from the shed.

Please _____ the fish on Monday.

Don't _____ the eggs on the floor.

_____ me a story before I go to bed.

Sentence practice

Mum wants Joe to tidy his bedroom. Write <u>two</u> suitable **commands**.

_____

_____

Revision 1

1 Underline the <u>three</u> words in each sentence that need a **capital letter**.

sam and lucy met sita at the corner shop.

i think josh was going to spain for his holiday.

gran and grandad always go shopping on monday morning.

Does harry live in hobbs lane?

2 Add the **punctuation mark** needed to complete these sentences.

Can I come and play_____

Put the paper in the printer_____

Today it rained all day_____

What a shock_____

3 Each sentence has a word missing. Write the full **sentence** so it makes sense.

He put on his coat went outside.

_____

Once upon a time there a little goat.

_____

4 Choose the correct word, '**and**', '**then**' or '**finally**', to complete each sentence. Write it in the space.

First wash your face. _____ get dressed.

Have some toast _____ drink your milk.

_____, brush your teeth _____ put on your coat.

5 Write the **plural** of these words.

gate _____   tree _____

bench _____   owl _____

railing _____   flower _____

bush _____   fox _____

6 Choose the correct word to complete each sentence.
Write it in the space.

The _____ dropped his brush.   (painting painter painted)

He is _____ up the litter.   (picking picker picked)

They _____ for hours.   (waiting waiter waited)

I _____ football yesterday.   (playing player played)

7 Add **un–** to these **verbs**.

___load   ___pack   ___tie

Now write a **sentence** using each new verb you have made.

_____

_____

_____

8 Rewrite each question as a **command**.

Could you get me a drink of water?

_____

Do you want to come and play at my house?

_____

15

Writing task 1

An exciting day

Write about an exciting day you enjoyed. Choose an idea from the pictures, or use one of your own. Your task is to say what happened and to make it sound exciting.

Before you start writing, think about:

- what happened
- what you saw or what you did
- what made it exciting

Remember

- Write in sentences.
- Use correct punctuation.
- Check your work carefully.

My exciting day

Nouns and noun phrases

Nouns are words that name things, such as 'man', 'dog' or 'bus'.

The dog barked at the bus.

A **noun phrase** is made up of the noun and any other words that go with it.

The dog chased a police car.

Try it

1   Underline all the **nouns** in these sentences.

The waiter carried the tray to the table.

The lady counted the money in her purse.

The man sat on a bench in the park and waited.

The little boy dropped the sweets on the floor.

The elephant has a trunk and large ears.

2   Complete each sentence using <u>two</u> suitable **nouns**.

Dad is digging a _____ in the _____ .

Emma rode her _____ round the _____ .

The girl put the _____ on the _____ .

The bird sat on the _____ of a _____ .

The fox sat by the _____ watching the _____ .

Sentence practice

Write a sentence about a cat in the garden. Use at least <u>three</u> **nouns**.

Adjectives

Try it

1 Underline all the **adjectives** in these sentences.

The angry bees buzzed around the tree.

The king wore his new crown to the party.

The pirate had a parrot with green feathers.

She sailed across the sea to a strange land.

The little mouse hid in the long grass.

2 Complete each sentence by adding a suitable **adjective** to the nouns in **bold**.

The _____ **wolf** showed his _____ **teeth**.

My cat Felix is a _____ **cat** and a _____ **cat**.

The giant lived in a _____ **house** with a _____ **door**.

The _____ **waves** crashed on to the _____ **rocks**.

The boy took the _____ **path** into the _____ **woods**.

Sentence practice

Write a sentence about a clown, using <u>two</u> or more **adjectives**.

_____

_____

Adjectives with suffixes –ful, –less

Some **adjectives** are made by adding the **suffixes –ful** or **–less** to a word.

careful   Prince Herman was a **careful** man.
careless   Prince Edgar was a **careless** man.

Try it

1   Use the **suffix –ful** or **–less** to make each word into an **adjective**. Write the adjective.

wonder _____   peace _____

forget _____   home _____

speech _____   hate _____

spot _____   wish _____

2   Complete each sentence by making an **adjective** ending with **–ful** or **–less**.

The doctor said a broken arm can be pain_____.

A moth is a harm_____ insect.

The small boy was power_____ against the mighty dragon.

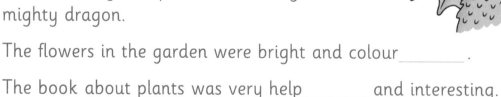

The flowers in the garden were bright and colour_____.

The book about plants was very help_____ and interesting.

Sentence practice

Add the **suffixes –ful** and **–less** to the word 'use'. Write two sentences, one for each of the **adjectives** you make.

_____   _____

_____   _____

20

Adjectives with suffixes –er, –est

Remember

You can use **adjectives** to compare things by adding the **suffixes –er** or **–est**.

George was strong. Jude was stronger.
Jed was the strongest of all.

Try it

1 Add the **suffixes –er** and **–est** to these **adjectives**. Write the new adjectives.

soft _____ _____

slow _____ _____

loud _____ _____

brave _____ _____

happy _____ _____

2 Choose the correct word to complete each sentence. Write it in the space.

He is the _____ man in all the land. (rich richer richest)

Rosie is _____ than her sister. (old older oldest)

Merlin was the _____ wizard of all. (wise wiser wisest)

A car is _____ than a bike. (quick quicker quickest)

My room is _____ than yours. (small smaller smallest)

Sentence practice

Add the **suffixes –er** and **–est** to the word 'fast'. Write <u>two</u> sentences, one for each of the **adjectives** you make.

_____

_____

Joining words: 'when', 'because'

The words 'when' and 'because' are joining words.
They join together two ideas in one sentence.
They help to give more information in a sentence.

The lion sniffed the air.
The lion sniffed the air because he could smell food.
The lion sniffed the air when he woke up.

Try it

1 Choose the best **joining word**, **'because'** or **'when'**, to complete each sentence.

The teacher was tired _____ she got home.

I am shivering _____ I am cold.

Amaya yawned _____ she woke up.

I like fruit _____ it is good for you.

Dad won first prize _____ his cake was the best.

2 Complete these sentences.

The tiger roared when _____

The king was happy because _____

William laughed when _____

She did not sleep because _____

He was reading his book when _____

Sentence practice

Write a sentence about a melting ice cream. Use one of the **joining words 'because' or 'when'**.

Joining words: 'if', 'that'

Remember

The words 'if' and 'that' are **joining words**. They join together two ideas in one sentence. They help to add more detail about the main idea in a sentence.

My sunflower will grow if I water it every day.
I hope that it will grow really tall.

Try it

1 **Complete each sentence using the joining word 'if' or 'that'.**

I would keep very still _____ I saw a snake.

Megan told me _____ I was in the team.

My dog starts to bark _____ it hears a noise.

I like stories _____ they are funny.

The man boasted _____ he was clever.

2 **Complete these sentences.**

I will give you a bag of gold if _____

The boy was so frightened that _____

I will help if _____

I am glad that _____

The man promised that _____

Sentence practice

Complete this sentence. Use one of the joining words 'that' or 'if'.

I feel sad _____

Compound nouns

A **compound noun** is made up of two words pushed together.
The two words together make one new noun.

footpath   daylight   bluebird

Try it

1 Add another word to make a **compound noun**.

play_____   _____house

goal_____   _____chair

star_____   _____stand

head_____   _____ball

snow_____   _____cake

2 Complete the **compound nouns** so that each sentence makes sense.

On his seventh birth_____ Christopher took his new _____board

to the play_____ .

Hannah left her hand_____ at the _____market check_____ .

In the biggest bed_____ , there was a purple _____case next to

the fire_____ .

A sign_____ pointed to the water_____ , where we saw a

beautiful rain_____ .

Sentence practice

Write a sentence about a trip to the beach, using <u>three</u> or more
compound nouns.

_____

_____

Commas in lists

Remember

You use **commas** to separate items in a list. With the last two items, you use 'and' instead of a comma.

The little elephant squirted water over the lion, the monkey, the rhino and the snake.

Try it

1 Add the missing **commas** to each sentence.

Mum makes plum strawberry and blackberry jam.

Blackbirds eat insects worms and berries.

We saw ducks geese swans and moorhens on the river.

You need paper scissors glue paints and a big box.

The leaves were red yellow orange and brown.

2 Add <u>three</u> more items to each list. Use the correct **punctuation**.

The farmer keeps sheep, cows_____

For dinner there was chicken_____

Dad went to buy apples_____

In the toy box I found marbles_____

Put the plates_____

Sentence practice

Write a sentence with a list of <u>three</u> or more foods that you like. Check your **punctuation**.

_____

_____

Verbs with –ing: present tense

In the **present tense**, you use the **–ing verb** form with the 'helper' verbs '**am**', '**is**' or '**are**'. These verbs show that an action is carrying on for some time.

I am waiting for my mum.
Amit is putting on his coat.
The twins are gazing out of the window.

Try it

1   Complete each sentence using the correct form of the **verb**.

They are _____ a hole.   (dig)

The boy is _____ the drum.   (bang)

We are _____ to play hockey.   (learn)

I am _____ my milk.   (drink)

My sister is _____ at me.   (smile)

2   Complete each sentence in the **present tense**, using the **–ing** form of a **verb**.

The ducks _____ on the pond.

The clock in the hall _____ .

The farmer _____ the hens.

Vikesh _____ for a walk.

I _____ for the bus.

Sentence practice

Write a sentence about what you are doing right now, using an **–ing verb** form.

_____

Verbs with –ing: past tense

In the **past tense**, you use the **–ing verb** form with the 'helper' verbs 'was' or 'were'. These verbs show that an action was carrying on for some time.

It was raining. James was reading.
Katie and Beth were drawing pictures.

Try it

1 Decide if each sentence is in the **past tense** or the **present tense**. Write 'past tense' or 'present tense'.

He is going to the shops.   _____

The stars were shining brightly.   _____

The tap was dripping in the sink.   _____

I am baking a cake for tea.   _____

Omar and Jess are having lunch.   _____

2 These sentences are in the present tense. Rewrite them in the **past tense**.

The man is pointing at me. _____

The eagles are flying. _____

I am looking for you. ___ _____

The boys are playing. _____

Dad is talking to us. _____

Sentence practice

Write a sentence in the **past tense** to say what Red Riding Hood was doing in the woods.

Revision 2

1 Underline the <u>three</u> **nouns** in each sentence.

A clock stood in the corner of the room.

A giraffe has a long neck that can reach the top branches.

The old woman was polishing the windows with a yellow duster.

The little boy went to fill the bucket at the well.

2 Underline the **adjective** in each sentence.

The little pony jumped over the fence and galloped off.

The clever rabbit tricked the crocodile.

The parrot stretched his beautiful wings.

Where did I put my green bag?

3 Underline the **verbs** in each sentence.

It was cold this morning so I wore my thickest socks.

I have a new game and I play it all the time.

The old man smiled when he hung the painting on the wall.

I read my book and then I go to bed.

4 Use **un–** to change the meaning of the underlined **adjective** in each sentence. Write the new adjective.

The race was <u>fair</u>.   _____

Joel was the <u>lucky</u> little boy.   _____

The children were <u>friendly</u> at her new school. _____

5 Write the missing **punctuation mark** to complete each sentence.

How amazing_____

I am planning a party_____

How did he do it_____

What a surprise_____

She went for a run_____

Do you like peas_____

6 Draw lines to match each sentence to the correct **sentence type**.

The thief is getting away. ●

Stop that man. ●

Leah has a meeting. ●   ● | statement |

Meet me on the corner. ●   ● | command |

Don't run on the grass. ●

7 There is a **punctuation mark** missing from this writing. Rewrite it correctly.

Class 3 went swimming Simon swam right across the pool.

_____

_____

8 These **verbs** are in the **present tense**. Rewrite them in the **past tense**.

We <u>mix</u> the pudding in the bowl.   _____

I <u>bake</u> a pie and Mum <u>makes</u> a cake.   _____ _____

Mum <u>passes</u> me a sandwich and I <u>eat</u> it.   _____ _____

Writing task 2

My favourite animal

Write about your favourite animal. Choose one from the pictures, or think of one of your own. Your task is to describe the animal and to explain why you chose it.

Before you start writing, think about:

- describing your animal
- what you know about your animal
- why it is your favourite

Remember

- Write in sentences.
- Use correct punctuation.
- Check your work carefully.

My favourite animal

Adverbs

Remember

An **adverb** is a word that tells you more about how an action is carried out.

She <u>opened</u> the back door <u>slowly</u>.
She <u>called</u> **softly** into the moonlight.

Try it

1 Underline the **adverb** in each sentence.

The door slid silently open.

She rocked the baby gently as she sang.

I placed the book carefully on the shelf.

We sat happily and watched the rabbits play.

The cat purred and swished her tail lazily.

2 Rewrite each sentence, adding a suitable **adverb**.

Flags flap in the wind. _____

The firework went off. _____

Dad turned off the leaky tap. _____

The sick child moaned. _____

Tom made his way home. _____

Sentence practice

Write a sentence using the **adverb** 'quietly'.

_____

_____

Adverbs with suffix –ly

You can make lots of **adverbs** by adding the **suffix –ly** to an **adjective**.

Mr Hodges was kind.   (adjective)
He spoke kind<u>ly</u>.   (adverb)

Try it

1   Add the **suffix –ly** to each **adjective** to make it into an **adverb**.
    Write the adverb.

brave   _____   sweet   _____

proud   _____   smooth   _____

smart   _____   bad   _____

sad   _____   selfish   _____

secret   _____   safe   _____

2   Choose the best **adverb** from the activity above to complete
    each sentence.

The lifeguard dived _____ into the water.

Grandpa dressed _____ in his best suit.

The plane landed _____ on the runway.

The team played _____ in the second half.

She wore the medal _____ for the rest of the day.

Sentence practice

Make the **adjective** 'fierce' into an **adverb**. Use the adverb to
write a sentence.

_____

Apostrophes in shortened forms

Remember

Sometimes two words are pushed together to make one word. Some letters are missed out. You write an **apostrophe** in place of the missing letters.

I am coming. ⟶ I'm coming.
Do not laugh. ⟶ Don't laugh.

Try it

1   Rewrite each underlined shortened word with the **apostrophe** in the correct place.

I have	Ive	_____	she is	shes	_____
was not	wasnt	_____	they will	theyll	_____
I would	Id	_____	we are	were	_____
cannot	cant	_____	he would	hed	_____

2   Write the underlined words as <u>one</u> word, using an **apostrophe**.

It <u>has not</u> been raining for long. _____

<u>I will</u> be home soon. _____

I think <u>it is</u> a great idea. _____

<u>It has</u> been a long time. _____

I <u>could not</u> help it. _____

Sentence practice

Write the words 'did not' as <u>one</u> word with an **apostrophe**.
Use the word in a sentence.

_____

Apostrophes for possession

You use an **apostrophe** with **–s** to show that something belongs to someone or something.

Cinderella's glass slipper   the giant's sack of gold

Try it

1   Underline the word that has an **apostrophe** to show that something belongs to someone or something.

I haven't seen Daniel's book.

Don't eat Baby Bear's porridge.

Holly's jumper isn't here.

I didn't hear the teacher's whistle.

I can't find the cat's collar.

2   Rewrite the sentence, adding an **apostrophe** with **–s** to show that something belongs to someone or something.

Cinderella sisters were mean. _____

This is Jason bag. _____

Is this Mum plate? _____

Tara hair is black. _____

I found my sister pen. _____

Sentence practice

Write a sentence to describe a hat belonging to a wizard, using an **apostrophe**.

_____

Nouns with suffixes –er, –ness, –ment

Some **nouns** are made by adding a **suffix** to the end of another word.

painter   sadness   statement

Try it

1 Add the correct **suffix, –er, –ness** or **–ment**, to make each word into a **noun**.

enjoy_____   teach_____

sick_____   play_____

work_____   fair_____

amaze_____   punish_____

shy_____   amuse_____

2 Add the correct **suffix** to complete the word in **bold**.

Jogging helped Sarah improve her **fit**_____.

The **garden**_____ cut the grass.

I was dazzled by the **bright**_____ of the sunlight.

He went to hospital for **treat**_____.

Dad wrote a **remind**_____ about the milk.

Sentence practice

Add a **suffix** to make the word 'kind' into a **noun**. Write a sentence using the noun you have made.

_____

_____

Proper nouns

A **proper noun** is a special noun that you use to name a person, place or thing. A proper noun always starts with a **capital letter**.

I met Adam Smith and his brother Jamie outside Hill Street School.

Try it

1 Underline all the **proper nouns** in these sentences. Give them a **capital letter**.

I think harry is in mr jackson's class at marshmead school.

We watched a film of neil armstrong taking off in apollo 11.

Once upon a time, king marcus lived in rockington palace.

We went to chester zoo with mr davies.

Mum said mrs patel moved to grove road in june.

2 Rewrite each sentence, using **proper nouns** in place of the underlined noun phrases. Remember to use **capital letters**.

A man went to town. _____

The teacher helped the boy. _____

The girl lived in a cottage. _____

The boy goes to school. _____

Sentence practice

Write a sentence with two **proper nouns** in it.

_____

Plural nouns and verbs

A **noun** can be **singular** (just one) or **plural** (more than one). You need
to use the correct **verb** to follow a singular or plural noun.

The bird **has** flown away. The birds **have** flown away.
The morning **feels** cold. The mornings **feel** cold.
The tree **is** turning gold. The trees **are** turning gold.

Try it

1   Choose the correct **verb** to follow each **plural noun**.

The boys _____ as they run into the playground.   (shout shouts)

Two buses _____ coming down the road.   (is are)

Bulls _____ sharp horns.   (has have)

The toys _____ in the box.   (go goes)

The flowers _____ in the garden.   (grow grows)

2   Rewrite each sentence, making the underlined **noun** a **plural**. Use
the correct **verb**.

The <u>hen</u> is clucking. _____

The <u>fox</u> sleeps in a den. _____

The <u>house</u> is very old. _____

The <u>baby</u> has blue eyes. _____

The <u>clown</u> was funny. _____

Sentence practice

Write a sentence using the **verbs** 'run' and 'runs'.

_____

Checking tense

When you write, you usually keep to the same **tense** all through a piece of writing. Always check that the **verbs** show the correct tense.

Leo **met** his friends and they ~~play~~ **played** football all afternoon.

Try it

1   Underline the **verbs** in each sentence. Tick the box if the sentence keeps to the same **tense**.

Jake jumped off the swing and ran to the slide. ☐

Ladybirds eat greenfly and lived for about two years. ☐

Anya sat by the river and she sees a beautiful swan. ☐

He walked along the road and heard a crash. ☐

Noah scrubbed the washing and hangs it on the line. ☐

2   Complete each sentence using a **verb** in the correct **tense**.

Elijah saw his friends and he _____ .

I was late but they _____ for me.

The farmer gets up early and he _____ the cows.

Andrew rolled over and he _____ back to sleep.

Spring is coming and the bears _____ up.

Sentence practice

Write a sentence to follow this one. Keep to the same **tense**.

Sophie looked up when she heard the car. _____

_____

Longer noun phrases

In longer **noun phrases**, you add words to the **noun** to give more detail about it. You can add **adjectives** before the noun or other details after the noun.

the green jumper
the large, blue jumper
the red jumper with the stars

Try it

1 Complete these **noun phrases**.

the _____ _____ box on the shelf

the _____ _____ butterfly

the little house _____

the orange flowers _____

the smart red car _____

2 Write <u>four</u> **noun phrases** to describe different dogs. One has been done for you.

the little fluffy dog in the basket

_____

_____

_____

_____

Sentence practice

Write a sentence about Annie's coat, using a longer **noun phrase**.

_____

Writing with joining words

You can use **joining words** to help improve your writing. Joining words can join two ideas together to make one longer **sentence**.

My dog likes to run around outside **but** he does not like having a bath. I take him for a walk every day **because** he needs lots of exercise.

Try it

1 Complete each sentence with a suitable **joining word**. Use a different one each time.

Dad got in the car _____ he drove to work.

She tried on the shoe _____ it did not fit.

Craig was crying _____ he was lost.

Rebecca hopes _____ she will win the game.

Cross the road _____ you see the cars stop.

2 Write each pair of sentences as <u>one</u> sentence, using a **joining word**.

Sonia went to the dentist. She had a bad tooth.

_____

I know it is home time. I hear the bell ring.

_____

Sentence practice

Write <u>two</u> sentences about reading books. Use a **joining word** in each one.

_____

_____

Revision 3

1 Write this sentence with the correct **punctuation**.

My brother has been to Spain France and Italy.

_____

2 Add a suitable **adjective** to complete each sentence.

An elephant is _____ than a mouse.

The sun is the _____ thing in the sky.

An orange is _____ than a lime.

Ava is the _____ girl in our class.

3 Use a **joining word** to complete each sentence. Use '**or**', '**but**', '**that**' or '**if**'.

She ran so fast _____ he could not catch her.

The glass will break _____ you drop it.

Eat your lunch _____ you will be hungry.

I want to stay up _____ it is late.

4 Use all of these nouns to make <u>five</u> **compound nouns**. Write each new compound noun.

table   paper   _____

news   barrow   _____

gold   rope   _____

wheel   cloth   _____

tight   fish   _____

5 Add a **suffix** to make each word into an **adjective**.

spite_____   end_____   play_____

Now use the **adjectives** to complete these **noun phrases**.

the _____ little kitten

the mean and _____ man

the _____ list of jobs

6 Complete each sentence using the **–ing** form of a **verb**.

I was wiping the table and Leon _____ the dishes.

It is raining and I _____ wet.

It happened when Dad _____ the car.

We saw a fox when we _____ the dog.

7 Rewrite each sentence using an **adjective** to describe the **noun**.

I saw a spider. _____

What a room! _____

There was a storm. _____

She had three brothers. _____

8 Complete these sentences.

I wanted an ice cream but _____

I need my gloves because _____

Sita ran home when _____

Dad will take us to the fairground if _____

Writing task 3

The magic potion

Write what happened when someone drank a magic potion. Choose an idea from the pictures, or use one of your own. Your task is to describe what happened and to make it interesting.

Before you start writing, think about:

● what kind of potion it was

● what happened to the person who drank it

● what happened afterwards

Remember

- Write in sentences.
- Use correct punctuation.
- Check your work carefully.

The magic potion

Progress chart

Tick the circle when you can do what the statement says.

Section 1

◯ I can write a series of sentences.

◯ I can punctuate a series of sentences with capital letters and full stops (or '?' or '!').

◯ I can write sentences using 'and', 'but', 'or'.

◯ I can use verbs in the present tense and the past tense.

◯ I can write and use statements.

◯ I can write and use questions.

◯ I can write and use exclamations.

◯ I can write and use commands.

Section 2

◯ I can use adjectives with nouns to make noun phrases.

◯ I can use the suffixes –ful, –less, –er and –est to form adjectives.

◯ I can use the words 'when', 'because', 'if' and 'that' to extend a sentence.

◯ I can form and write compound nouns.

◯ I can use commas in between the items in a list.

◯ I can use the –ing form of verbs in the present tense and the past tense.

Section 3

◯ I can make adverbs ending with –ly and use them in sentences.

◯ I can use an apostrophe to show the missing letters in words like 'don't'.

◯ I can use an apostrophe to show that something belongs to someone.

◯ I can use the suffixes –ness, –ment, –er to form nouns.

◯ I can say which words are proper nouns and begin them with capital letters.

◯ I can use the correct verb after a singular or plural noun.

◯ I can check verbs to make sure I keep to the same tense.

◯ I can write and use longer noun phrases.

Glossary

adjective a 'describing word' that tells you more about a noun (for example, a red car)

adverb a word that says how an action is performed (for example, He walked slowly. She ran quickly.)

apostrophe a punctuation mark used in shortened forms (for example, can't) or to show that something belongs to someone (for example, Sam's hat)

capital letter a special letter (for example, A, B, C, D) used at the start of sentences or for proper nouns and 'I'

comma a punctuation mark used to separate items in a list (,)

command a type of sentence that tells someone to do something (for example, Write your name.)

compound noun a noun made up of two smaller words put together to form one word (for example, footpath)

exclamation a type of sentence that shows strong feeling and ends with an exclamation mark (for example, What a surprise!)

exclamation mark a punctuation mark used at the end of an exclamation (!)

full stop a punctuation mark used at the end of a sentence (.)

joining word a word that joins two ideas together in one sentence (for example, and, but, if, when)

noun a word that names things (for example, car, dog, man)

noun phrase a noun and the other words that go with it (for example, the fast police car)

past tense the tense used when an action or event has already happened

plural more than one of something (for example, cats, dogs, foxes)

present tense the tense used when an action or event is happening now

proper noun a noun used to name a person, place or thing, which starts with a capital letter (for example, Chris, London, Friday, April)

punctuation special marks used in writing to help the reader (for example, full stops, commas, question marks)

question a type of sentence that asks for information or needs a response, and which ends with a question mark (for example, Who are you?)

question mark a punctuation mark used at the end of a question (?)

sentence a group of words put together to say something, which must make sense, start with a capital letter and end with a full stop (or '?' or '!')

singular just one of something (for example, cat, dog, fox)

statement a type of sentence that gives information or tells you something (for example, Roses are red.)

suffix a group of letters added to the end of a word to make a different word (for example, –er, –ful, –ness)

tense the form of a verb, which tells you when the action happened – in the past or the present

verb a 'doing word' (for example, play, run, skip) or 'being word' (for example, is, was, has, have)

Schofield&Sims

the long-established educational publisher specialising in maths, English and science

Schofield & Sims Grammar and Punctuation is a whole-school scheme that supports a structured approach to teaching and learning these fundamental literacy skills. Comprising six pupil books and six teacher's guides, this comprehensive programme enables pupils to gain a secure understanding of grammar and punctuation as they progress from the identification of individual parts of speech and punctuation marks to the composition of complex multi-clause sentences and paragraphs. Through engaging lessons and practice activities, pupils encounter each grammar point in a range of contexts, enabling them to develop an awareness of the nuances of language and the ability to communicate effectively.

Each pupil book provides:
- full curriculum coverage
- a user-friendly summary of the key learning point for each lesson
- plenty of practice, from short activities that check understanding to more in-depth questions that require pupils to compose their own sentences
- regular revision pages to reinforce learning and identify strengths and weaknesses
- varied writing tasks to promote the application of new knowledge
- a self-evaluation checklist to encourage pupils to assess their own learning
- a glossary to support the confident use of grammatical terminology.

The accompanying teacher's guides contain lesson plans, answers to all the questions in the pupil book, and assessment and record-keeping resources. A selection of free downloads is also available.

Grammar 2 covers the National Curriculum requirements for Year 2, including sentence types; verbs (past and present tense); more joining words; the progressive form; commas in lists; apostrophes used for possession and shortened forms; nouns and noun phrases, plural nouns and verbs; adverbs; adjectives; and suffixes.

Grammar 1	ISBN 978 07217 1390 8	**Grammar 1 Teacher's Guide**	ISBN 978 07217 1391 5
Grammar 2	ISBN 978 07217 1392 2	**Grammar 2 Teacher's Guide**	ISBN 978 07217 1393 9
Grammar 3	ISBN 978 07217 1394 6	**Grammar 3 Teacher's Guide**	ISBN 978 07217 1395 3
Grammar 4	ISBN 978 07217 1396 0	**Grammar 4 Teacher's Guide**	ISBN 978 07217 1397 7
Grammar 5	ISBN 978 07217 1398 4	**Grammar 5 Teacher's Guide**	ISBN 978 07217 1399 1
Grammar 6	ISBN 978 07217 1400 4	**Grammar 6 Teacher's Guide**	ISBN 978 07217 1401 1

ISBN 978-07217-1392-2

9 780721 713922 >

MIX
Paper from responsible sources
FSC® C023114
www.fsc.org

ISBN 978 07217 1392 2
Key Stage 1
Age range 5–7 years
£3.50 (Retail price)

For further information and to place your order visit
www.schofieldandsims.co.uk or telephone 01484 607080